Time Pieces for Trumpet

Volume 1

1588 Buffens

from *Orchesographie*

Thoinot Arbeau
(1520–1595)

1610 Magnificat

from *Vespers of 1610*

Claudio Monteverdi
(1567–1643)

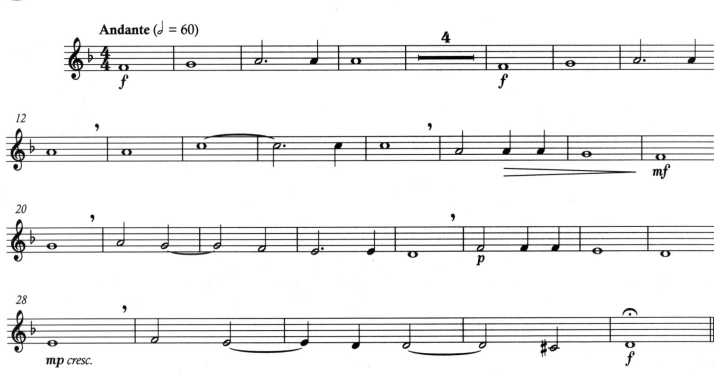

AB 2492

1651 Dance

Anon.

from *The English Dancing Master*

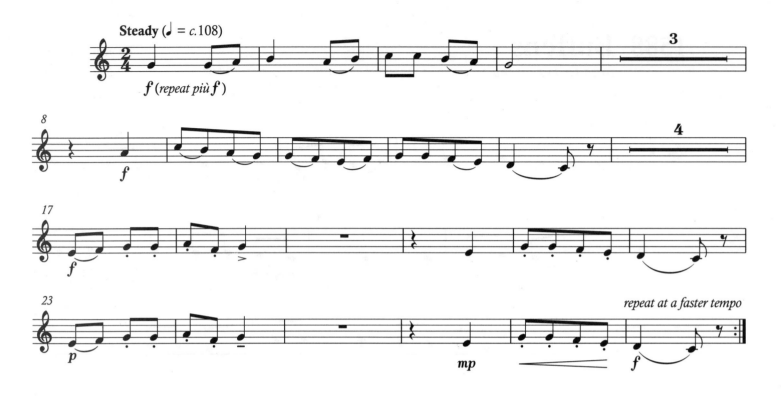

1694 Come, ye Sons of Art

Henry Purcell
(1659–1695)

*Alternative notes have been provided in brackets where the original notes exceed the range required for Grade 1.

1715 Minuet

from *The Water Music*

George Frideric Handel
(1685–1759)

Allegretto (♩ = *c.*116)

f (*repeat* **mf**)

f (*repeat più f*)

(**rit.** *2nd time*)

1724 Ein' feste Burg

from Cantata No. 80

Johann Sebastian Bach
(1685–1750)

Moderato (♩ = *c.*88)

f

cresc. *mf*

rall.

f

1732 Allegretto
from Fantasia No. 4

Georg Philipp Telemann
(1681–1767)

1740 Menuet

Louis-Claude Daquin
(1694–1772)

AB 2492

1776 Allegro
from Divertimento in C, K. 188

Wolfgang Amadeus Mozart
(1756–1791)

1812 Allegretto
from Symphony No. 7

Ludwig van Beethoven
(1770–1827)

1828 Ecossaise

Johann Nepomuk Hummel
(1778–1837)

Jauntily (♩ = c.120)

1830 Ländler
from *Processional Fanfare*

Anton Diabelli
(1781–1858)

Allegretto (♩. = c.60)

AB 2492

1851 Andante

Louis Köhler
(1820–1886)

Andante (♩ = 60)

c.1860 Come to me (Spiritual)

Anon.

Lento molto espressivo (♩ = c.76)

1878 Song of the Peasant

from *Album for the Young*

Peter Ilyich Tchaikovsky
(1840–1893)

Adagio (♩ = *c.*66)   (The peasant is trying out his accordion)

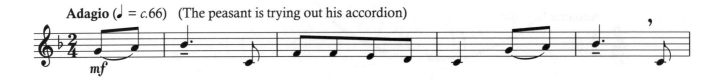

*c.*1885 March

Adolf Müller
(1801–1886)

Allegro moderato (♩ = *c.*144)

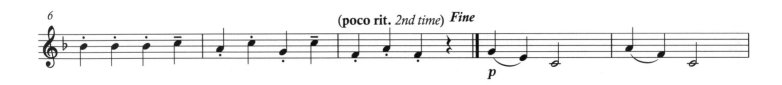

1893 Shadows

Vassili Kalinnikov
(1866–1901)

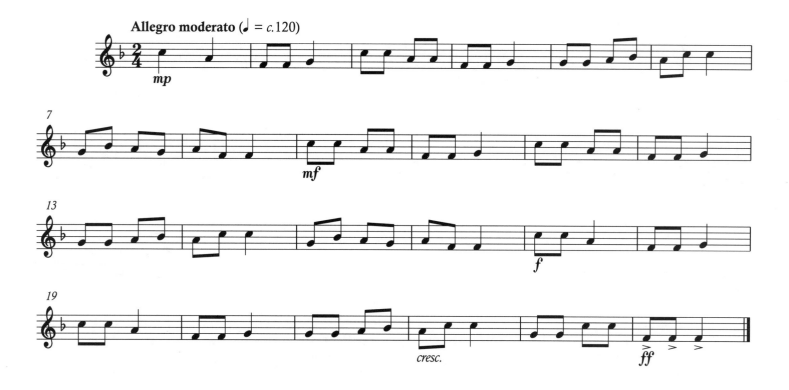

1924 Campanae Parisienses

Ottorino Respighi
(1879–1936)

1940 The Silent Lake

from *Duets for Children*

William Walton
(1902–1983)

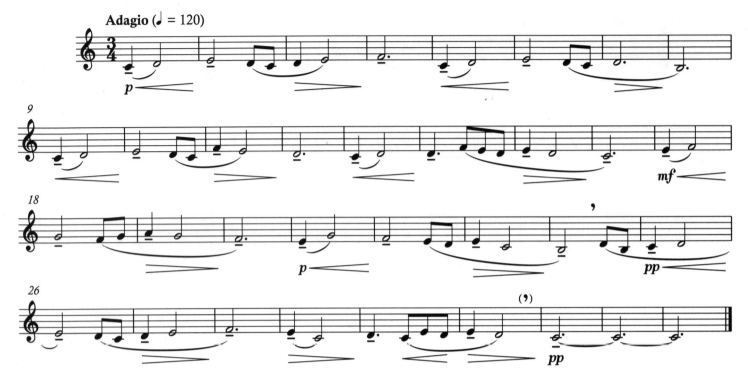

1946 Play

from *For Children*, Vol. I

Béla Bartók
(1881–1945)

AB 2492

1991 March of the Trumpet Teachers

Paul Harris

Time Pieces

for
Trumpet

Music through the Ages in 3 Volumes

Volume 1

**Selected and arranged by
Paul Harris and John Wallace**

**The Associated Board of
the Royal Schools of Music**

CONTENTS

Time Pieces for Trumpet

Volume 1

1588 Buffens

from *Orchesographie*

Thoinot Arbeau
(1520–1595)

AB 2492

1610 Magnificat
from *Vespers of 1610*

Claudio Monteverdi
(1567–1643)

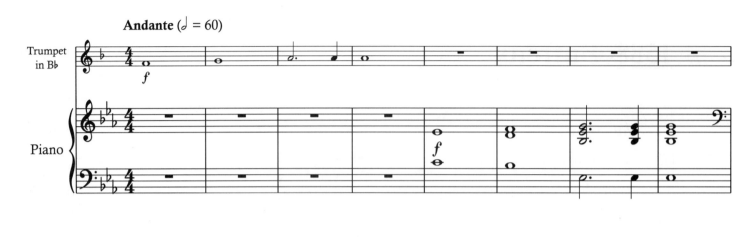

1651 Dance

from *The English Dancing Master*

Anon.

repeat at a faster tempo

1694 Come, ye Sons of Art

Henry Purcell
(1659–1695)

*Alternative notes have been provided in brackets where the original notes exceed the range required for Grade 1.

1715 Minuet

from *The Water Music*

George Frideric Handel
(1685–1759)

1724 Ein' feste Burg

from Cantata No. 80

Johann Sebastian Bach
(1685–1750)

1732 Allegretto

from Fantasia No. 4

Georg Philipp Telemann
(1681–1767)

AB 2492

1740 Menuet

Louis-Claude Daquin
(1694–1772)

1776 Allegro

from Divertimento in C, K. 188

Wolfgang Amadeus Mozart
(1756–1791)

1812 Allegretto

from Symphony No. 7

Ludwig van Beethoven
(1770–1827)

AB 2492

1828 Ecossaise

Johann Nepomuk Hummel
(1778–1837)

1830 **Ländler**

from *Processional Fanfare*

Anton Diabelli
(1781–1858)

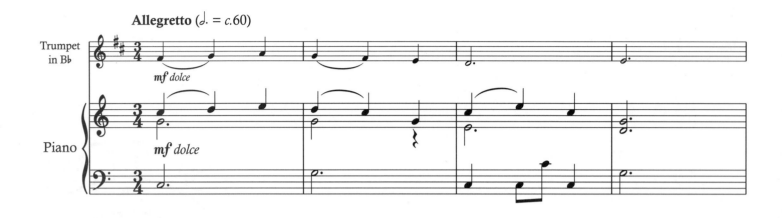

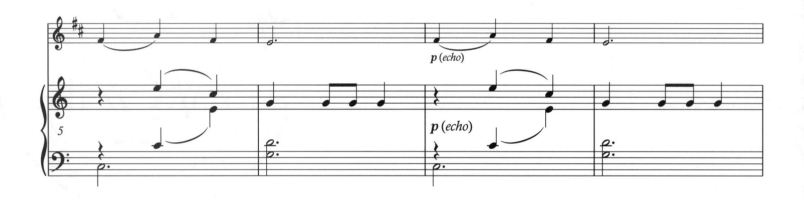

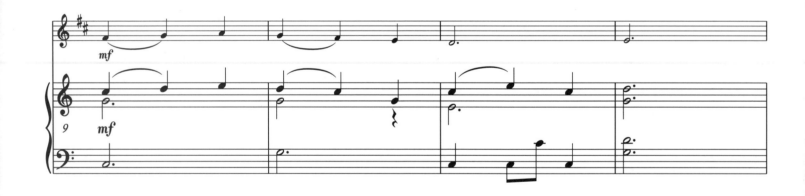

AB 2492

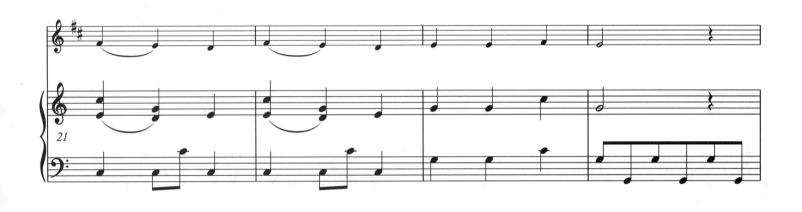

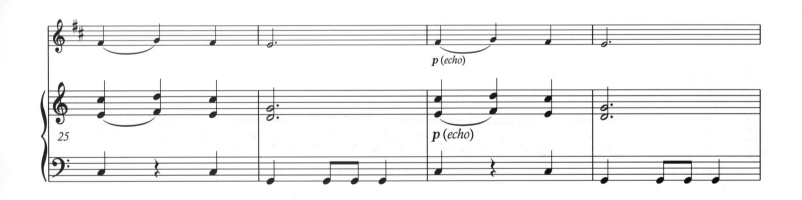

1851 Andante

Louis Köhler
(1820–1886)

*c.*1860 Come to me (Spiritual)

Anon.

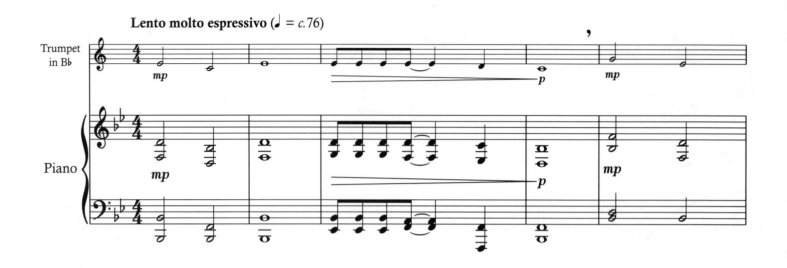

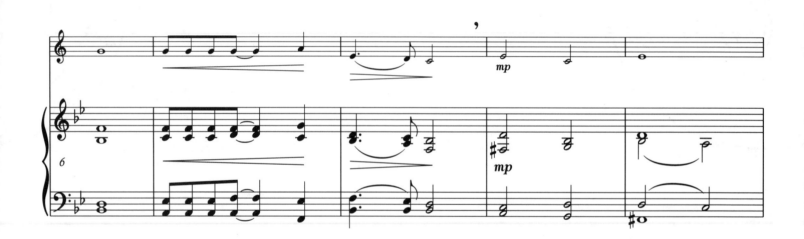

<u>1878</u> Song of the Peasant

from *Album for the Young*

Peter Ilyich Tchaikovsky
(1840–1893)

c.1885 March

Adolf Müller
(1801–1886)

1893 Shadows

Vassili Kalinnikov
(1866–1901)

1924 Campanae Parisienses

Ottorino Respighi
(1879–1936)

Andante mosso (♩ = 100)

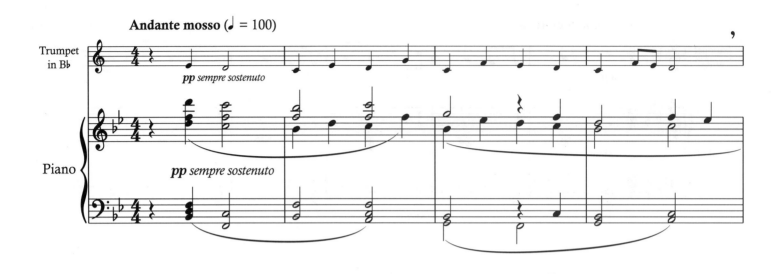

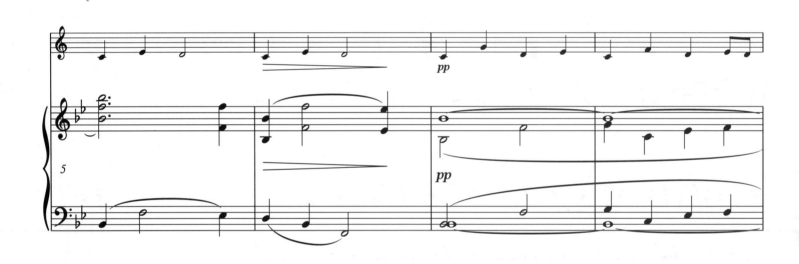

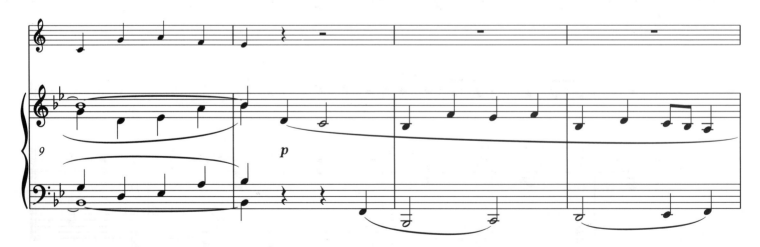

AB 2492

1940 The Silent Lake

from *Duets for Children*

William Walton
(1902–1983)

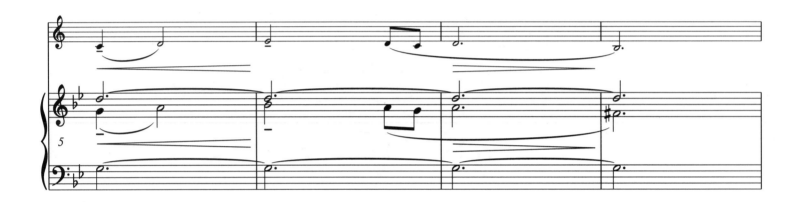

AB 2492

1946 Play

from *For Children*, Vol. I

Béla Bartók
(1881–1945)

1991 March of the Trumpet Teachers

Paul Harris

AB 2492

Music origination by
Barnes Music Engraving Ltd, East Sussex
Printed by Halstan & Co Ltd, Amersham, Bucks, England